Hard up

by Ann Ruffell

AXIS education

Acknowledgements

Cover design: Oliver Heath, Rafters Design

Illustrations on pages 15, 17, 19, 29, 31, 33 and 39 © Paul Gardiner, 2005. The right of Paul Gardiner to be identified as the illustrator of this work has been asserted by him in accordance with the Copyright, Design and Patents Act, 1988.

Brinsford books are a direct result of the findings of a two-year authoring/research project with young offenders at HMYOI Brinsford, near Wolverhampton. Grateful thanks go to all the young people who participated so enthusiastically in the project and to Judy Jackson and Brian Eccleshall of Dudley College of Technology.

First published in Great Britain by Axis Education Ltd

ISBN 1-903685-93-1

Axis Education PO Box 459
Shrewsbury SY4 4WZ

Email: enquiries@axiseducation.co.uk

www.axiseducation.co.uk

Deb had no work.

She had no cash.

She did not have cash for her baby.

She could not buy stuff for the baby.

It cost a lot.

The gas was off.

She could not pay.

It was cold.

Her giro came.

She was glad.

There was cash for the baby.

She could get food.

5

But Jack came.

He hit Deb.

He made the baby cry.

He hit the TV.

He took the cash.

Now Deb had no cash for food.

She had no cash for the baby.

She had no cash for gas.

The TV was bust.

She saw a bag in the street.

There was cash in the bag.

Deb took the bag.

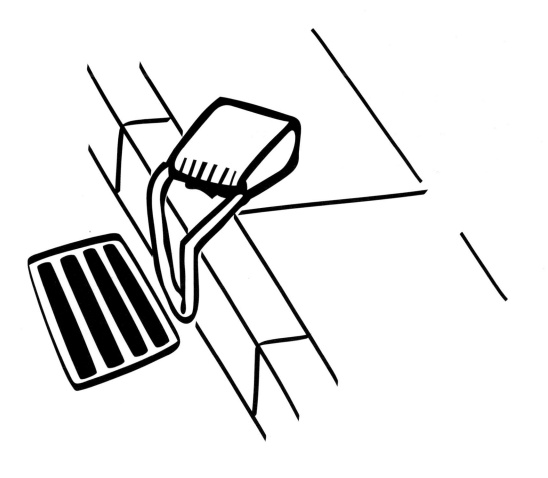

Deb went to the shop.

She came home with food.

It was okay for two days.

But then the cash ran out.

Deb went out to a shop.

She put tins in a bag.

She did not pay for them.

No one saw.

Now Deb had food.
The baby had food.

She went to a new shop.
It was not hard.
No one saw her.

But she had to pay the rent.

She had no TV.

She had to have cash.

Her Mum could not help.

Deb could have food but no cash.

Viv could not help.

Viv had no cash.

But she had a TV.

Deb could stop and see it with Viv.

Deb went to a shop.

There was a lot of make-up.

She could put it in her bag.

No one saw.

She put the make-up in the pram
with the baby.

Some of her mates would pay for make-up.

Liz gave her cash for make-up.

Now she had cash for food.

But no cash for gas.

It was cold.

Deb went back to the shop.

She took more make-up.

No one saw.

More of her mates gave her cash for make-up.

Now Deb could pay for gas.

Jack came back.

It was a bit of a shock.

He hit Deb.

He made the baby cry.

He took the rest of the make-up.

He took some tins of food

and all her cash.

Deb was gutted.

But what could she do?

Jack was big.

His mates were big.

Deb could not win.

She had to nick some more stuff.

She left the baby with her Mum.

She took some CDs.

A bell rang.

Deb ran off.

She ran fast.

No one saw it was her.

But Jack came by

in a car with his mates.

They took the CDs
and other stuff
from her flat.

Her Mum said she should not put up with it.
Jack was a bad lot.

Her mates said she should not put up with it.
She should call the police.

Deb saw her Mum was right.
She saw her mates were right.
It was bad to hit the baby.

She was fed up with Jack.

She was fed up when he hit her.

She called the police.

The police went to see Jack.

He had the CDs

and lots more stuff.

Jack and his mates
were put in the nick.
Now Deb was safe.

When her giro came
She had cash for food.
She had cash for the gas
and the TV.

Deb and her mates had a good time.
She did not have to nick stuff now.
And she was safe from Jack.

Glossary

baby   a very young child

giro   money from the government for someone who is unemployed, ill or who has a very low income

mates   friends

police   the organisation that protects against crime and enforces the law